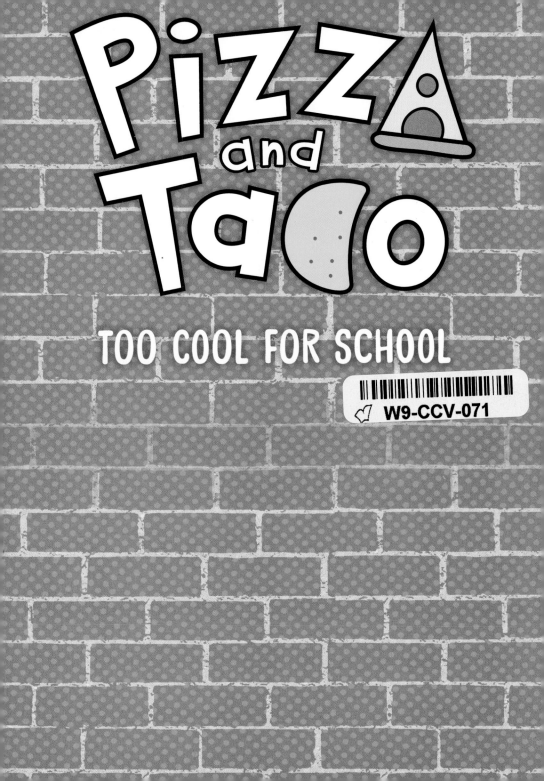

Pizza and Taco

TOO COOL FOR SCHOOL

Pizza and Taco

TOO COOL FOR SCHOOL

STEPHEN SHASKAN

WE are going to be the coolest kids in school.

SCHOLASTIC INC.

To Finn and Stella, two cool kids

ISBN 978-1-338-86708-4

12 11 10 9 8 7 6 5 4 3 2 1   22 23 24 25 26 27

Printed in the U.S.A.   40

First Scholastic printing, September 2022

Contents

Chapter 1
Coolest Kids in School

4

6

Chapter 2
The New Kid

15

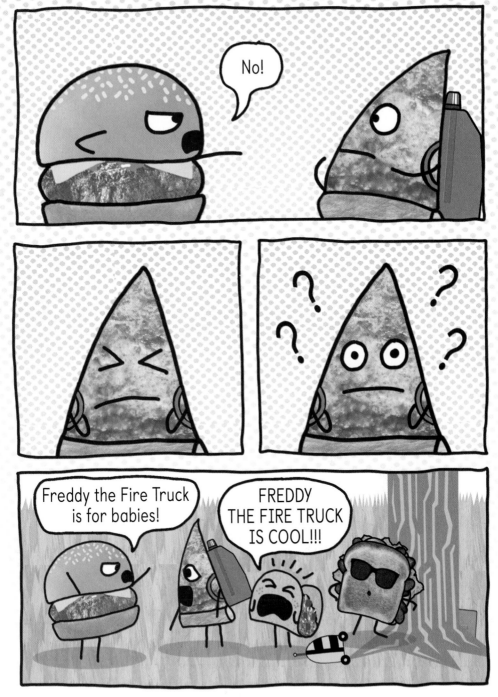

19

21

22

23

Chapter 3
Late for Class

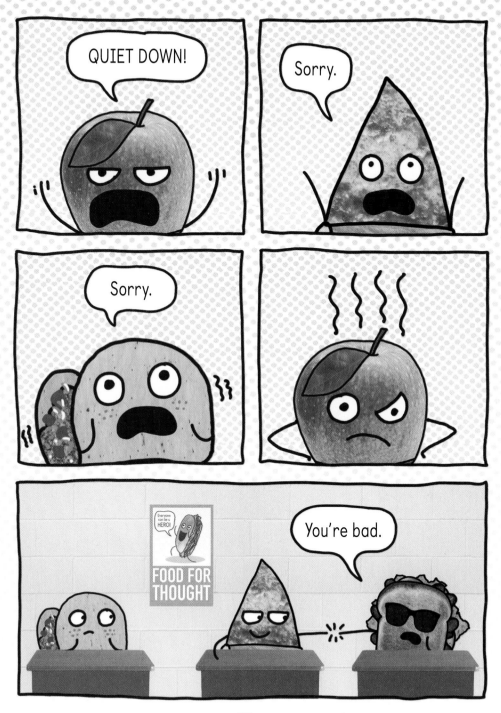

28

31

37

Chapter 4
Late for Class, Again

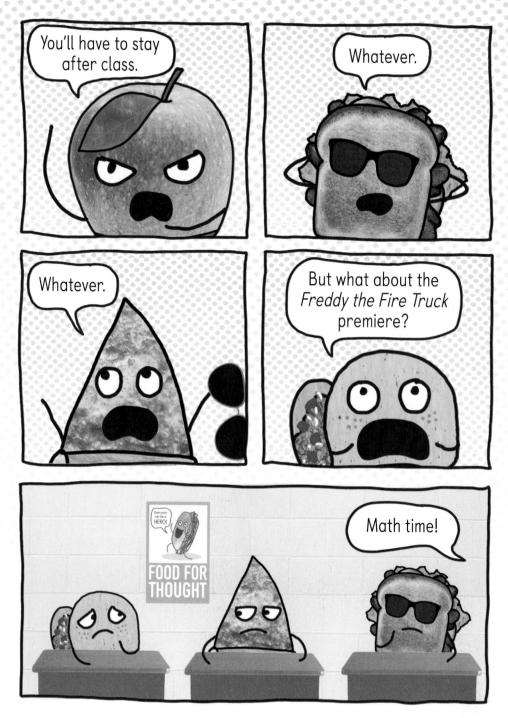

46

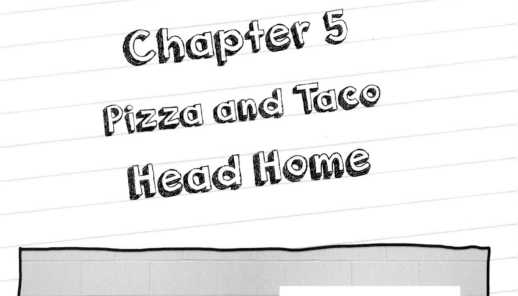

Chapter 5
Pizza and Taco
Head Home

48

49

51

53

54

55

Karl Raschke

STEPHEN SHASKAN is the author-illustrator of the Pizza and Taco series and more than a dozen other children's books. His debut picture book, *A Dog Is a Dog,* was a New York Public Library 100 Titles for Reading and Sharing Selection and a CCBC Choices Book. Stephen holds a BFA in illustration from Rhode Island School of Design, and worked with kids for twenty years as an early-childhood educator. He performs musical story times; presents at schools, conferences, and festivals; and teaches comic classes to kids. Stephen lives with his wife and frequent collaborator, Trisha Speed Shaskan, in Minneapolis.